Y0-BZY-113

Colouring Book of Krishna

Colouring Book of Krishna

Colouring Book of Krishna

Colouring Book of Krishna

Colouring Book of Krishna

Colouring Book of Krishna

Colouring Book of Krishna

Colouring Book of Krishna

Colouring Book of Krishna

Colouring Book of Krishna